W9-ARO-049

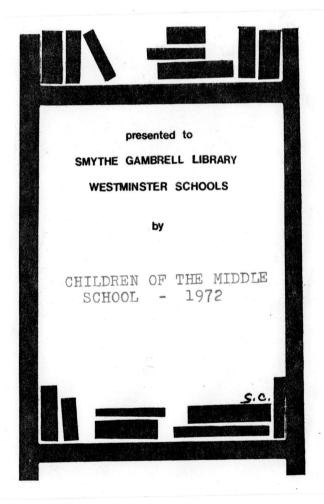

presented to

SMYTHE GAMBRELL LIBRARY

WESTMINSTER SCHOOLS

by

CHILDREN OF THE MIDDLE
SCHOOL — 1972

S.C.

SMYTHE GAMBRELL LIBRARY
WESTMINSTER ELEMENTARY SCHOOLS
1424 WEST PACES FERRY RD., N. W.
ATLANTA, GA. 30327.

*I thought I heard
the city*

I thought I heard the city

Lilian Moore

Collage by Mary Jane Dunton

ATHENEUM   1969   NEW YORK

SMYTHE GAMBRELL LIBRARY
WESTMINSTER ELEMENTARY SCHOOLS
1424 WEST PACES FERRY RD., N. W.
ATLANTA, GA. 30327

J
811
Moore

Text Copyright © 1969 by Lilian Moore
Collage Copyright © 1969 by Mary Jane Dunton
All rights reserved
Library of Congress catalog card number 69-18964
Published simultaneously in Canada by
McClelland & Stewart, Ltd.
Manufactured in the United States of America
Printed by Connecticut Printers, Inc., Hartford
Bound by H. Wolff, New York
Designed by Mary Jane Dunton
First Edition

To Beatrice de Regniers

11892

POEMS

*I thought I heard
the city*

THE BRIDGE

A bridge
by day
is steel and strong.
It carries
giant trucks that roll along
above the waters
of the bay.
A bridge is steel and might —
till night.

A bridge
at night
is spun of light
that someone tossed
across the bay
and someone caught
and pinned down tight—
till day.

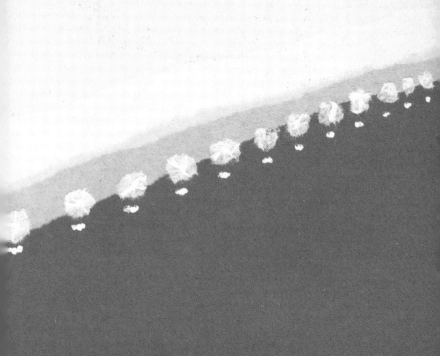

THE TREE ON THE CORNER

I've seen
the tree on the corner
in spring bud
and summer green.
Yesterday
it was yellow gold.

Then a cold
wind began to blow.
Now I know —
you really do not see
a tree
until you see
its bones.

NIGHT SNOW

A ghostly snow
floats
out of the sky
tonight,
and snow moths
dance
in the pale street light.

SNOWY MORNING

Wake
gently this morning
to a different day.
Listen.

There is no bray
of buses,
no brake growls,
no siren howls and
no horns
blow.
There is only
the silence
of a city
hushed
by snow.

PIGEONS

Pigeons are city folk
content
to live with concrete
and cement.

They seldom
try
the sky.

A pigeon never sings
of hill
and flowering hedge,
but busily commutes
from sidewalk
to his ledge.

Oh pigeon, what a waste of wings!

CONSTRUCTION

The giant mouth
chews
rocks
spews them
and is back for
more.

The giant arm
swings up
with a girder
for
the fourteenth floor.

Down there,
a tiny man
is
telling them
where
to put a skyscraper.

REFLECTIONS

On this street
of windowed stores
see,
in the glass
shadow people meet
and pass
and glide to
secret places.

Ghostly mothers
hold
the hands of dim gray children,
scold
them silently
and melt away.

And
now and then,
before
the window mirror
of a store,
phantom faces
stop
and window shop.

ROOFSCAPE

The lines are
straight
and
many-cornered —
plunging,
rising high.

From my window
I can see
how roofs
design a sky.

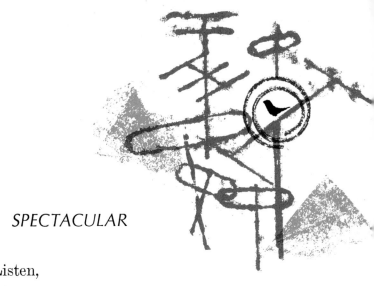

SPECTACULAR

Listen,
a bird is singing.
Look,
up there!
He's on the rooftop
clinging
to the TV aerial,
singing
on prime time —
and no sponsor!

"THINK OF TREE"

Under
the car smell

over
the tar smell

a sweet green and far smell
flows
down the street.

And it says
drifting by,
    "Think of tree.
     Think of sky.
     Think of ripe apples
     and hay, sun-dry."

Then you know —
not far away
they are cutting grass
in the park today.

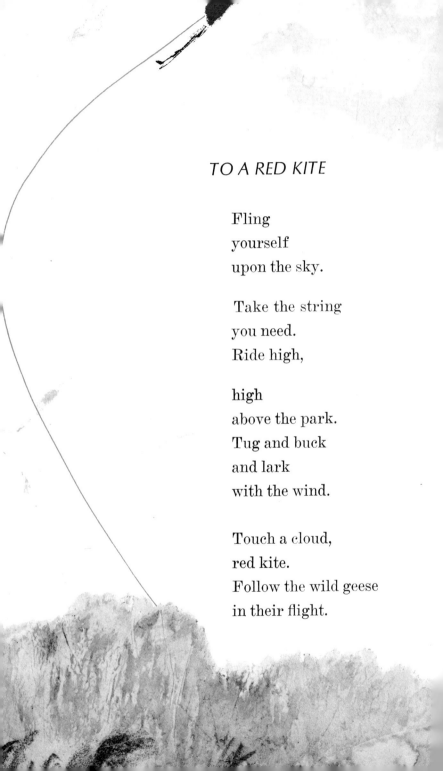

TO A RED KITE

Fling
yourself
upon the sky.

Take the string
you need.
Ride high,

high
above the park.
Tug and buck
and lark
with the wind.

Touch a cloud,
red kite.
Follow the wild geese
in their flight.

FOGHORNS

The foghorns moaned
    in the bay last night
  so sad
  so deep
I thought I heard the city
    crying in its sleep.

WINTER DARK

Winter dark comes early
mixing afternoon
and night.
Soon
there's a comma of a moon,

and each street light
along the
way
puts its period
to the end of day.

Now
a neon sign
punctuates the dark
with a bright
blinking
breathless
exclamation mark!

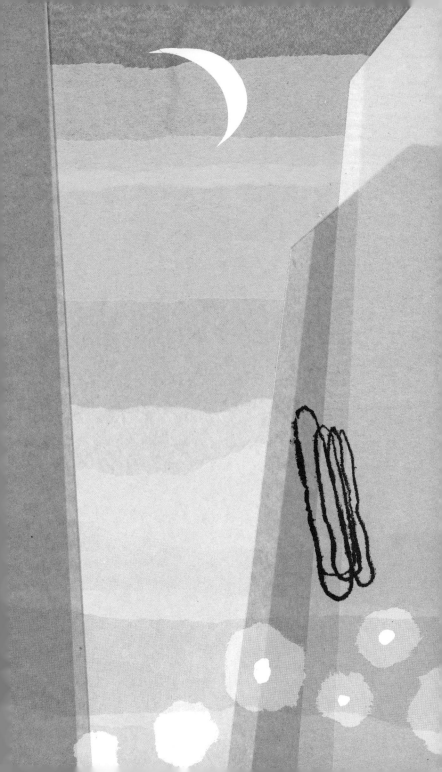

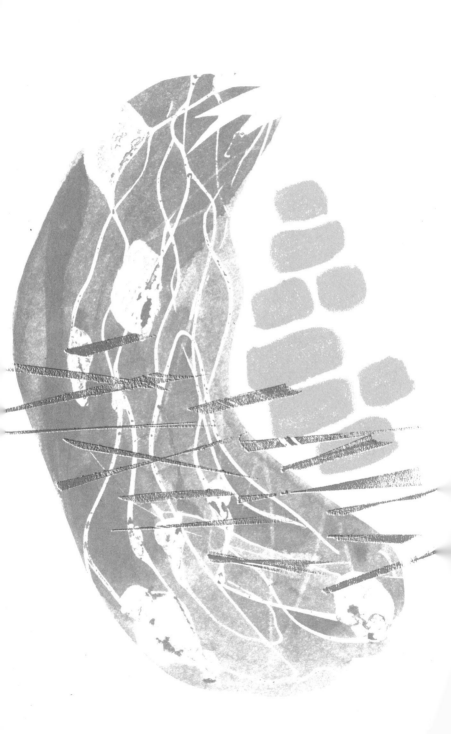

RAIN POOLS

The rain
litters
the street
with mirror splinters
silver and
brown.

Now
each piece
glitters with

sky
cloud
tree

upside down.

SUMMER RAIN

The sky is
scrubbed
of every smudge of
cloud.

The sidewalk is a
slate
that's quickly
dry.

Light
dazzles
like
a washed
window pane,

and
I

breathe
the freshly laundered
air
of after-rain.

FORSYTHIA BUSH

There is nothing
quite
like the sudden
light

of
forsythia
that
one morning
without warning

explodes
into yellow
and
startles the street
into spring.

SHELLS

The bones of the sea
are on the shore,
shells
curled into the sand,
shells
caught in green weed hair.
All day I gather them
and there are always
more.

I take them home,
magic bones of the sea,
and when
I touch one,
then I hear
I taste
I smell the sea
again.